ISBN 978-0-545-61959-2

10 9 8 7 6 5 4 3   20 21 22 23 24

Printed in the U.S.A.   40

This edition first printing 2020

Illustrated by Stacy Peterson

Designed by Janet Kusmierski

BFF
Secrets
My Lips Are Sealed

BY MEGAN FAULKNER

Scholastic Inc.

Table of Contents

OATH OF SECRECY

Fill in the blanks and take turns repeating the following:

I,_____,in the

presence of _____,

on this _____ day of _____ (month),

_____(year), do solemnly swear that

I will faithfully execute the position of

Best Friend Forever

to _____and will, to the best

of my ability, preserve, protect, and

defend the secrets written

in the pages of this book.

_____

Signature

OATH OF SECRECY

Fill in the blanks and take turns repeating the following:

I,_____, in the

presence of _____,

on this _____ day of _____ (month),

_____(year), do solemnly swear that

I will faithfully execute the position of

Best Friend Forever

to_____and will, to the best

of my ability, preserve, protect, and

defend the secrets written

in the pages of this book.

_____

Signature

Quiz: Are Secrets Safe With You?

Check True or False to the following questions, then turn the page to see how you score:

T or **F**

1. People come to me to get the latest gossip.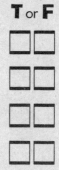

2. I'm told I am a good listener.

3. I sometimes speak without thinking.

4. I am often referred to as a social butterfly.

5. I prefer to have a few close friends rather than a lot of acquaintances.

6. I try to think about other people's feelings as well as my own.

7. It's wrong to talk about people behind their backs.

8. It's important to keep your promises.

9. Some people are too nice.

10. I feel jealous when something really good happens to someone else.

11. I've had a lot of best friends.

12. I don't worry about what people think of me, I just try to be myself.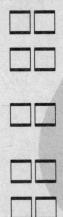

13. I can talk my way out of any situation.

14. Being a member of the "popular crowd" is overrated.

15. I get jealous if my BFF starts spending more time with another friend.

16. I am lucky to have good friends in my life.

17. I love being the center of attention.

18. I've known some of my closest friends my whole life.

19. I change my attitude and behavior depending on who I'm with.

20. It's easy to be a good friend—just treat others as you would like to be treated.

Scoring: *Add or subtract points based on your answer to each question.*

1) T - 5, F + 5		11) T - 5, F + 5
2) T + 4, F - 4		12) T + 4, F - 4
3) T - 3, F + 3		13) T - 2, F + 2
4) T - 3, F + 3		14) T + 5, F - 5
5) T + 5, F - 5		15) T - 3, F + 3
6) T + 5, F - 5		16) T + 5, F - 5
7) T + 4, F - 4		17) T - 4, F + 4
8) T + 5, F - 5		18) T + 3, F - 3
9) T - 2, F + 2		19) T - 4, F + 4
10) T - 2, F + 2		20) T + 5, F - 5

25 POINTS OR LESS

RED ALERT! Secrets are NOT safe with you! It's time to take a good look at your actions and priorities. Everyone wants to be liked, but telling and sharing secrets to feel popular is a slippery slope. People will come to you to get the latest gossip—until it's about *them*. Once they realize you'll talk about *anyone* behind their back, people won't trust you as much! Practice not sharing what someone tells you, especially if they ask you not to.

26–50 POINTS

GOOD JOB. You try to be a good friend to others and appreciate the friends you have. You feel happy and special when someone confides in you. Sometimes you cave under peer pressure and tell something you shouldn't. You feel bad about it, but in that moment, you just want to feel like part of the group! Start resisting the urge to participate in behavior you know is wrong. At the end of the day, maintaining the trust of your closest friends is far more rewarding than enjoying a few seconds in the spotlight.

51 POINTS OR HIGHER

GOLD MEDAL BFF! Congratulations—you are the dream best friend. You understand that true friendship is based on loyalty, respect, trust, and empathy. When someone tells you a secret, they know it's 100 percent safe. Your friends are truly blessed to have someone like you in their lives.

TOP SECRET FACTS ABOUT ME

1. My greatest fear is: _____

2. I am most proud of: _____

3. My biggest regret is: _____

4. The person I love more than anyone else is:

   _____

5. If I could be anywhere in the world right now it would be:

   _____

6. If I could go back in time I would: _____

   _____

7. If a genie granted me three wishes they would be:

   1) _____

   2) _____

   3) _____

8. The person who frustrates me the most is:

   _____

9. If I had to spend the rest of my life with only one person

   on a desert island, it would be _____,

   because _____.

10. I wish I could be more like: _____

TOP SECRET FACTS ABOUT ME

1. My greatest fear is: _____

2. I am most proud of: _____

3. My biggest regret is: _____

4. The person I love more than anyone else is:

   _____

5. If I could be anywhere in the world right now it would be:

   _____

6. If I could go back in time I would: _____

   _____

7. If a genie granted me three wishes they would be:

   1) _____

   2) _____

   3)_____

8. The person who frustrates me the most is:

   _____

9. If I had to spend the rest of my life with only one person

   on a desert island, it would be _____,

   because _____.

10. I wish I could be more like: _____

Should You Tell Your Secret?

How many times have you told someone a secret and regretted it later? If the answer is "more than once," you should be thinking longer and harder about what to share and what to keep to yourself. Whether you are thinking of telling your own secret, or passing along someone else's, ask yourself the following questions:

1. Is it dangerous?

If someone is putting herself in physical danger or threatening to physically harm someone else, you must tell an adult. Tell your teacher or your parent or guardian. You may feel like a tattletale, but you'll feel worse if you say nothing and someone gets hurt.

2. Is it mean?

Hurting someone's feelings is often just as damaging as hurting them physically. If someone tells you something mean about someone else, be the bigger person and have it stop with you. Spreading rumors about someone is a form of bullying.

3. Is it worth sharing?

Some people like to create rumors or exaggerate stories to get attention and create drama. If the secret sounds unbelievable, it probably is.

4. Why do I want to share it?

Passing along or sharing a secret to look cool and feel popular are the worst reasons. Try to stick to information that everyone benefits from, like if you hear you're getting a surprise guest visitor at school that day.

Record your wishes, cut them out, and keep them somewhere safe, like in a diary, time capsule, or wish jar.

I Secretly Wish . . .

1. I could eat as much _____

   and _____ as I want.

2. Adults would stop telling me to "_____

   _____."

3. I could sleep in until _____ every day.

4. _____ would come up to me and

   say "_____

   _____

   _____."

5. I could be more like _____.

6. I had the following superpowers: _____

   _____

7. _____ grew on trees.

8. I was better at _____.

9. I could forgive _____ for

   _____.

10. _____ would forgive me for

    _____

Record your wishes, cut them out, and keep them somewhere safe, like in a diary, time capsule, or wish jar.

I Secretly Wish . . .

1. I could eat as much _____

   and _____ as I want.

2. Adults would stop telling me to "_____

   _____."

3. I could sleep in until _____ every day.

4. _____ would come up to me and

   say "_____

   _____

   _____."

5. I could be more like _____.

6. I had the following superpowers: _____

   _____

7. _____ grew on trees.

8. I was better at _____.

9. I could forgive _____ for

   _____.

10. _____ would forgive me for

    _____

How Well Do You Know Your BFF?

Write your answers, then pass them to your friend to go through the list and add check marks for correct answers and Xs for incorrect answers in the boxes provided. Add up the check marks to get your score.

Correct?

Middle Name(s): _____ ☐

City of Birth: _____ ☐

Favorite Food: _____ ☐

Least Favorite Food: _____ ☐

Favorite Singer/Band: _____ ☐

Favorite Song: _____ ☐

Favorite Actor: _____ ☐

Favorite Movie: _____ ☐

Favorite Website: _____ ☐

Favorite Viral Video: _____ ☐

Favorite School Subject: _____ ☐

Least Favorite School Subject: _____ ☐

Secret Crush: _____ ☐

Dream Vacation: _____ ☐

Dream Career: _____ ☐

How Well Does Your BFF Know You?

Correct?

Middle Name(s): _____ ☐

City of Birth: _____ ☐

Favorite Food: _____ ☐

Least Favorite Food: _____ ☐

Favorite Singer/Band: _____ ☐

Favorite Song: _____ ☐

Favorite Actor: _____ ☐

Favorite Movie: _____ ☐

Favorite Website: _____ ☐

Favorite Viral Video: _____ ☐

Favorite School Subject: _____ ☐

Least Favorite School Subject: _____ ☐

Secret Crush: _____ ☐

Dream Vacation: _____ ☐

Dream Career: _____ ☐

Score:

Less than 5 correct: Whoa! Some major bonding time is needed. If you spend most of your time together doing sports or other group activities, book some downtime to just chill out and talk.

6-9 correct: The perfect balance! You have a strong friendship but still have space to be individuals.

10-15 correct: Do you finish each other's sentences? Are people confused when one of you shows up without the other? It's fun to have someone who feels like a twin, but it's also important to maintain the aspects of your personality that make each of you unique.

Secret Ways to Hide Your Stuff

Whether it's at home or at school, there always seem to be nosy people determined to uncover your secrets. Here are some suggestions for keeping your most private thoughts and belongings safe from prying eyes:

1. Decoy:

A decoy is used to distract someone from something else. Get a little notebook or diary and write a few fake entries. Hide it in a typical place like your sock drawer or under your mattress. Snoopers will find the decoy and think they've hit the jackpot. Meanwhile, your actual diary is safely hidden elsewhere.

2. Password-Protection:

Keep your journal on your computer and password-protect it. For further security, save your document in a folder protected with a *different* password. Instead of naming it "diary" and putting it in My Documents, name it something boring like "data 5," then save the folder somewhere unexpected.

3. Plain Sight:

Use a plain, old school notebook for a journal. Fill the first few pages with school notes. Keep the journal notebook stacked in a pile with other school books and papers.

4. Secret Code:

Write in a secret code that only you understand (see page 30). Even if your journal is found, no one will know how to read it!

5. Disguise:

Find a hardcover book with a dust jacket that is unlikely to be of interest to anybody—think a ten-year-old world atlas or *Video Game Codes 2006*. Remove the jacket and place it over your journal.

Slide loose papers between the pages of old books and return to your bookshelf.

Store bulkier items in boxes with misleading labels such as "Doll Clothes" and "Old School Assignments."

Our Totally Most Embarrassing Secrets

There's no way to avoid it—embarrassing things happen to all of us. The good thing is, they give you new stories to share with close friends. Write down your funniest moments here:

Most embarrassing thing to happen to me at school:

_____

_____.

Most embarrassing thing to happen to me in a public place:

_____

_____.

Most embarrassing thing to happen to me in front of my

BFF: _____

_____.

The most embarrassing thing I have ever said is:

_____

_____.

The most embarrassing thing a family member has ever said

or done is: _____

_____

_____.

Our Totally Most Embarrassing Secrets

There's no way to avoid it—embarrassing things happen to all of us. The good thing is, they give you new stories to share with close friends. Have your BFF write their funniest moments here:

Most embarrassing thing to happen to me at school:

_____

_____.

Most embarrassing thing to happen to me in a public place:

_____

_____.

Most embarrassing thing to happen to me in front of my

BFF: _____

_____.

The most embarrassing thing I have ever said is:

_____

_____.

The most embarrassing thing a family member has ever said

or done is: _____

_____

_____.

Sleepover Games

1. Two Truths and a Lie

Sitting in a circle, each person takes a turn saying three things about herself: two of these things should be true, and one should be a lie. The rest of the circle tries to guess which one is the lie. Here's a tip! Your lie should sound like it's true, like your favorite ice cream flavor is chocolate when it's really vanilla!

2. Never Have I Ever

Give each player a handful of small candies (the same amount each) and sit in a circle with a bowl in the middle. One person starts by saying something like: "I've never gone on a roller coaster." Everyone who also hasn't done that (and be truthful!) must put one of their candies in the bowl. At the end, the person with the most candies left wins all the candy in the middle.

3. Truth or Dare

In this familiar game, players choose between answering a question truthfully, or performing a "dare," both of which are set by the other players. Remember, questions and dares should ALWAYS be friendly and never mean.

Dare Suggestions:

- Sneak up behind someone and dance energetically for as long as you can go unnoticed.
- Walk along the sidewalk singing a song as loudly as possible.
- Try to keep a straight face while everyone else tries to make you laugh.
- Walk an invisible dog down the road and back.
- Hug a bunch of trees on your block and tell each one you love them.
- Try to lick your elbow.
- Let the person beside you do your makeup, blindfolded.

4. Telephone

To prepare, write a few messages that are at least ten words long down on paper. Sit players in a circle. The first player draws a message from the bowl. They must repeat the message to the next person by whispering it in their ear. They cannot pass on or show the message. The receiver turns to the next person and passes along what they heard. Continue around the circle or down the line. The last person to receive the message repeats what they heard aloud, and the first person reveals the original message.

CREATE SECRET CODES AND CIPHERS

Skilled as you may be at keeping letters and journals safe from snoops, mistakes happen, and your secrets can fall into the wrong hands.

A code is a secret language known only by the sender and receiver. A basic code involves the direct substitution of a regular word with a random word. For instance:

ORIGINAL WORD	CODE WORD
meet	sing
playground	gift shop
lunch	Christmas
notepad	cereal

Encrypted Message: Sing at the gift shop after Christmas with cereal.

Decrypted Message: Meet at the playground after lunch with notepad.

_____

_____

_____

_____

_____

_____

TRY MAKING YOUR OWN!

original word   code word

_____   _____

_____   _____

_____   _____

_____   _____

_____   _____

_____   _____

_____   _____

_____   _____

_____   _____

_____   _____

_____   _____

_____   _____

_____   _____

_____   _____

CREATE SECRET CODES AND CIPHERS

A cipher is a substitution of each letter of the alphabet with a different letter or symbol. Ciphers are unlocked using a key.

Alphabet: A B C D E F G H I J K L M N O P Q R S T U V W X Y Z
Key: Z Y X W V U T S R Q P O N M L K J I H G F E D C B A

Encrypted Message: NVVG NV ZG GSV YVZXS
Decrypted Message: meet me at the beach

Make your own! Don't feel limited to the regular alphabet. In place of letters, you can use pictures, emojis, animals—your imagination is the limit!

Alphabet: A B C D E F G H I J K L M N O P Q R S T U V W X Y Z
Key:

Encrypted Message:
Decrypted Message:

Alphabet: A B C D E F G H I J K L M N O P Q R S T U V W X Y Z
Key:

Encrypted Message:
Decrypted Message:

Alphabet: A B C D E F G H I J K L M N O P Q R S T U V W X Y Z
Key:

Encrypted Message:

_____

_____

_____

_____

_____

_____

Decrypted Message:

_____

_____

_____

_____

_____

_____

FOLDING SECRET NOTES

Little Square

The goal here is to make your note as small as possible:

Instructions

1. Take an 8.5" by 11" piece of paper and fold it lengthwise hot-dog style. Make sure the side with writing on it is facing the inside, so you can't see it. Fold the paper hot-dog style a second time so you have a long, thin piece of paper.

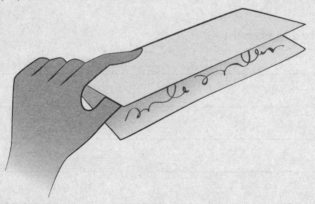

2. Fold one end up and the other end down. The ends will now look like triangles.

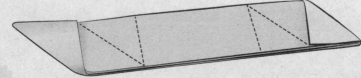

3. Fold the triangles again in the same direction on each side. Your paper will look like a sideways "s."

   **If you fold the triangles inward, you will get a rectangle, and this is wrong.

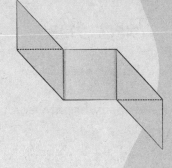

4. Fold each side inward, one side toward the back of the center square and the other side toward the front.

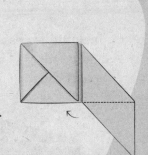

5. Fold the top triangle back toward the middle of the square and tuck it under.

6. Fold the bottom triangle forward and tuck in under.

   Finished!

Paper Star

You will need:

Strips of brightly colored or plain paper 8.5" long by 0.5" wide

1. Fold one end in a knot, leaving about half an inch excess.

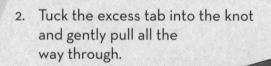

2. Tuck the excess tab into the knot and gently pull all the way through.

3. Fold down any additional excess.

4. Fold the long paper strip over.

5. Repeat step number 4 until you reach the end of the paper.

6. Tuck in the end of the paper.

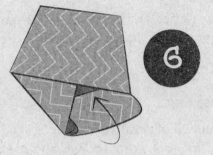

7. Push in the sides with your nail.

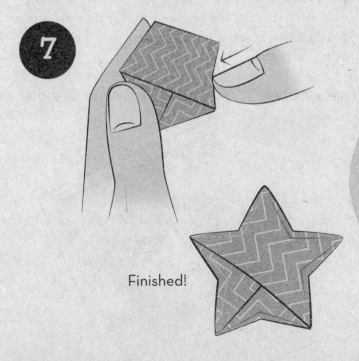

Finished!

BFF BOREDOM-BUSTERS

Love hanging out with your BFF but need a change from your usual activities? Try one of these!

1. WRITE A GRATITUDE LIST

Take the time to notice and appreciate both the obvious things (roof over your head) as well as the little things (the smell and warmth of fresh laundry).

2. BE ANONYMOUSLY NICE

Write down a bunch of positive messages like "You're Awesome!" or "You look great today!" and place them randomly around your school and neighborhood. Tape them to lampposts, tack them on community bulletin boards, stick them in the crack of a door—the sky's the limit. You'll feel great and chances are you'll brighten someone else's day.

3. SNAP A PICTURE TOGETHER EVERY HOUR FOR AN ENTIRE DAY

4. COME UP WITH NEW OUTFIT COMBINATIONS

Pull out your clothes and come up with some new outfit combos. You might have far more outfits than you realized!

5. VOLUNTEER TOGETHER

Collect blankets and towels for the local animal shelter; tutor younger students; or ask a guardian's permission to contact local historic sites, libraries, nursing homes, and day camps to see what kind of volunteer positions are available.

6. BUILD A TIME CAPSULE

Select a weather-resistant container (e.g., a stainless-steel thermos) and fill it with items like labels or packaging from common products, newspaper or magazine clippings, photographs, completed journals, printed e-mails, etc. Write a description of what it is like to live right now (i.e., day-to-day activities, trends, fashions, how much things cost, etc.). Put everything inside your time capsule and pick a place to bury it—but make sure you'll remember where it is! Ask an adult for permission before you dig a hole.

7. PUT GOOGLY EYES ON EVERYTHING IN THE FRIDGE

8. PLAN A WEEKLY EXERCISE SCHEDULE

Whether it's dancing in your basement, jogging around the school track, or signing up for tennis lessons, make a plan and stick to it. Reward yourself after each session with a delicious smoothie or other healthy treat.

9. WRITE A BIOGRAPHY OF SOMEONE

Everyone has an interesting story to tell. Interview a neighbor or family member. Make an audio or video recording as well as taking written notes. Take current photographs, but also ask them to lend you some of their old photos to scan (remember to return them!). Write your bio and give a copy to the subject.

10. BECOME EXPERTS IN SOMETHING

Choose something you're both interested in. Maybe it's a certain type of music; a new artistic skill, like sewing or calligraphy; a technical ability, like computer programming or portrait photography; something food-related, like how to bake the perfect chocolate-chip cookie or make an omelet—there are endless possibilities!

what do you secretly admire about your BFF?

Everyone has bad days. Who better than your closest friend to remind you of all the wonderful qualities and talents you possess? Fill out these pages for each other, cut them out, and read them over when you're feeling down.

Dear _____,

When I first met you, I knew we would become friends

because _____.

If I had to describe you in three words, they would be

_____, _____,

and _____.

I'm always amazed and impressed at how good you are at

_____, _____,

and _____.

In my opinion, the special qualities that make you unique are

_____.

The best part of being your friend is _____.

Yours sincerely,

_____

what Do you secretly Admire About your BFF?

Everyone has bad days. Who better than your closest friend to remind you of all the wonderful qualities and talents you possess? Fill out these pages for each other, cut them out, and read them over when you're feeling down.

Dear _____,

When I first met you, I knew we would become friends

because _____.

If I had to describe you in three words, they would be

_____, _____,

and _____.

I'm always amazed and impressed at how good you are at

_____, _____,

and _____.

In my opinion, the special qualities that make you unique are

_____.

The best part of being your friend is _____.

Yours sincerely,

_____

Quiz: Should You Tell?

Think about each secret and decide if it's something you should tell or not. Answer Yes or No. Check your answers on the following pages to learn more!

Y or **N**

1. Your friend is getting a new brother or sister. ☐☐

2. You broke something at home but no one saw you. ☐☐

3. You failed a test at school. ☐☐

4. You saw your friend steal something. ☐☐

5. Your BFF is moving away. ☐☐

6. A friend told you they have a secret crush on someone at school. ☐☐

7. Your sibling is begging you to tell them what they're getting for their birthday from your parents. ☐☐

8. Your friend is being bullied by another kid on the school bus but made you promise to keep it a secret. ☐☐

9. Your friend shared a rumor you know is false about another classmate or friend. ☐☐

10. Some of your classmates are planning to pull an embarrassing prank on another student. ☐☐

SCORING:

1. NO, that's something really special that your friend should be allowed to share herself.

2. YES, you should tell the owner of the item that broke. If you don't come clean, you're going to carry around the guilt, which will be worse than facing the consequences.

3. YES, you should tell your parents or guardian you failed a test at school. There's no reason to tell your classmates, but you should definitely tell your parents so they can help you figure out what went wrong and arrange help if you need it.

4. YES, you should definitely talk to your friend or tell a trusted adult if you saw your friend steal. Talk to your friend directly and tell her you're not comfortable being around someone who steals. If she doesn't seem sorry or willing to stop, consider telling a trusted adult.

5. NO, you shouldn't tell anyone yet that your friend is moving away. If you want to talk about it, consider talking to your parents, guardian, or trusted adult. Your friend is probably experiencing a lot of different emotions and should have the option to tell other people when she feels ready.

6. *NO*, you shouldn't tell anyone your friend's secret crush! This could be very embarrassing for both your friend and the crush if it becomes public knowledge. Other kids may tease both of them. What if the crush doesn't feel the same way? You must put your friend's feelings above the excitement of sharing it.

7. *NO*, you shouldn't tell anyone the gift they're going to receive from someone else! As much as the person is dying to know, the surprise will be much more exciting on the actual day.

8. *YES*, always speak up to a parent, teacher, or trusted adult when you see someone being bullied. Bullying is serious. Your friend might not think it's a big deal or may be embarrassed to have adults find out, but knowing and saying nothing puts you on the side of the bully. Tell your friend that if they don't tell an adult, you will.

9. *NO*, you shouldn't repeat a rumor your friend shared about someone else, whether you believe it or not.

10. *YES*, you should tell someone if your friend or classmates are planning an embarassing prank on someone. Wouldn't *you* want to know if someone was planning to make you a target? Pranks should be fun, not mean. If you think someone may get hurt or upset, try to put a stop to the prank.

20 Ways to Make Your BFF's Day

1. Invite her over for breakfast.

2. Bake cookies and bring her half the batch.

3. Invite her to a family event; she might decline, but will still feel honored.

4. Ask her what she wants to do next time you hang out and do whatever she suggests!

5. Help her clean up her room or finish other chores.

6. Plan a fun weekend activity to do together.

7. Give her a cool manicure.

8. Offer her an item of clothing you don't wear and say, "I think this would look better on you."

9. Send her a postcard in the mail.

10. Send her a cute photo of her favorite animal.

11. Give her compliments randomly and often.

12. Ask her how her day was and ask follow-up questions.

13. If something important is happening, wish her good luck beforehand and ask how it went right afterward.

14. If you go to school together, bring lunch for both of you.

15. Make a playlist of songs both of you like or have certain memories attached to.

16. Go watch her in a sporting event or performance and cheer her on.

17. Recommend a book you enjoyed and lend her your copy.

18. Randomly say "I'm so glad you're my friend."

19. Create an activity for you to do together once a week or month.

20. Surprise her with a memory jar from page 56 or a DIY gift from page 58.

Friendship Q & A

Q: I told my best friend a secret and she promised not to tell anyone. Someone came up to me later and asked if it was true—obviously she told my secret! How can I ever trust her again?

A: Sit down with your friend outside of school and tell her you are hurt and disappointed that she betrayed your confidence. If she seems genuinely sorry and apologizes, give her another chance to prove her trustworthiness. If she blows it off and doesn't see what the big deal is, it's time to reevaluate your friendship. If you can't trust your BFF, who CAN you trust?

Q: I'm really shy and my BFF is more outgoing. I feel safe and comfortable going to social events with her, but if she's not able to go somewhere with me, I won't go at all. I want to be comfortable by myself, but I'm worried people won't like me. What should I do?

A. It might feel like you're the only one who worries about people judging you, but the truth is, most people worry about this to an extent! If you're starting a new class, remind yourself that everyone else is worrying about the exact same thing you are. If no one talks to you, it's because they're hoping you'll talk to THEM. Just smiling and introducing yourself will be a relief to both of you.

Q: My friend is going through a really hard time, and I want to comfort her. How can I help?

A: There are times in life when you can't do anything to help a friend going through a rough time. What you CAN do is give her your undivided attention when she does reach out to you. Let her talk as long as she wants. Give her lots of hugs. Consider making her a Best Friend Survival Kit (see page 58).

Q: I have a friend who copies everything I do! If I buy a new top, she goes out and gets the same one. If I start a new hobby, she's suddenly interested in it, too. How can I get her to stop copying me without hurting her feelings?

A: As annoying as this is, your friend is copying you because she thinks you're cool and feels insecure about expressing her own taste. Say something to her like "I really love picking out clothes that reflect my personality. Can I help you with yours?" Spend time together looking through magazines and putting together possible looks. She'll start feeling more confident about her own abilities.

Q: My best friend and I have been inseparable for as long as I can remember. Lately, though, she'd rather sit around talking about crushes than do activities we've always done. I find it really boring. What can I do?

A: Developing new interests and growing out of others is a normal part of life. Rather than focus on what your BFF *doesn't* want to do anymore, plan more of the things you still do enjoy together—things like watching movies, baking cookies, or going to the beach. Meanwhile, start reaching out to other friends who have the same interests as you.

Secret Letters to Our Future Selves

Fill in the following and seal them in envelopes. On the outside of the envelope, write "DO NOT OPEN UNTIL ____" (whatever year you've chosen).

Store your envelopes somewhere safe, like with your class photos and other memorabilia.

Dear _____,

It's me! Your _____ -year-old self! I want to tell you right away

that you look _____ today. That outfit is absolutely _____

and your hair is so _____ and _____. Today I

am wearing _____ and_____

because outside it is _____. I'm sitting here with

my best friend, _____. Are we still best friends? I

hope so. Are you still living in _____? Is your

favorite food still _____? I wonder if you are

studying _____ at school, or if you are already

working as a successful _____. I hope you are

happy and making all your dreams come true!

Love always,

_____

Secret Letters to Our Future Selves

Fill in the following and seal them in envelopes. On the outside of the envelope, write "DO NOT OPEN UNTIL ____" (whatever year you've chosen).

Store your envelopes somewhere safe, like with your class photos and other memorabilia.

Dear _____,

It's me! Your _____ -year-old self! I want to tell you right away

that you look _____ today. That outfit is absolutely _____

and your hair is so _____ and _____. Today I

am wearing _____ and _____

because outside it is _____. I'm sitting here with

my best friend, _____. Are we still best friends? I

hope so. Are you still living in _____? Is your

favorite food still _____? I wonder if you are

studying _____ at school, or if you are already

working as a successful _____. I hope you are

happy and making all your dreams come true!

Love always,

_____

Friendship Memory Keepers

1. Shadow Box

Shadow box frames are like regular picture frames except they have a space between the glass and the padded back panel.

Make a label to pin inside, such as "Best Friends Forever" or "Remember When."

Save concert tickets, movie-ticket stubs, photographs, amusement-park passes, birthday cards, etc.

2. Friendship Album

Take a picture together every year in the same place, at the same time of year, in similar outfits, and in the same pose.

3. Memory Jar

Write down your BFF memories on scraps of paper and save them in a special jar. At the end of the year, empty the jar and read them together. Start a new jar every year!

You will need:

- A large glass jar with a lid
- Glue
- Decorative items of your choice: fake flowers, stickers, beads, buttons, etc.

Instructions:

- Make a label for the jar (include the year).

- Decorate the jar. Use markers, glitter, or whatever you want!

- Start adding your memories! In addition to written memories, you can add movie-ticket stubs, photos, candy wrappers, little charms, greeting cards—whatever you want!

Easy DIY Gifts for Your BFF

Best Friend Survival Kit

When you can't be there in person to help your BFF through a tough time, this kit will show her you're still there in spirit!

You WILL NEED:

A cute box, bag, or tin

Suggestions for Contents:

- Her favorite chocolate bar or candy—to remember the sweet things in life

- Gum—because friends stick together through good and bad

- Band-Aids—for hurt feelings or a broken heart

- Eraser—to help start each day with a clean slate

- Pack of tissues—for tears of sadness and joy

- Crayons—to add color to the darkest day

- A small flashlight—to remember the light at the end of the tunnel

- Something with a happy face on it—because smiles are contagious

- Coupons for unlimited venting—because sometimes you just need to let it all out

- Lemonade mix—when life gives you lemons, make lemonade

- You can attach individual notes to each of the items, or list the contents and their meaning on a separate piece of paper.

Jumbo Paper Clip Bookmarks

Your friend will never lose her page with these cute bookmarks!

For six bookmarks, you will need:

6 jumbo plastic-coated paper clips (4" x 1")
8 yards of 1/4"-wide ribbon in different colors and patterns

Instructions:

1. Cut each yard into 12" lengths.

   For each clip:

2. Select one 12" piece of ribbon.

3. Loop one piece through the paper clip (use the end shown in the diagram), fold, and bring the ends together.

4. Tie two tight knots.

5. Repeat three times.

Monster Rock Magnets

These adorably silly rock monsters make great locker magnets or paperweights.

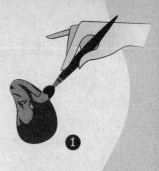

You will need:

- Smooth, light-colored stones, 2" or smaller
- Acrylic paints
- Medium-size and small paintbrushes
- Fine-tipped black permanent marker
- Strong (or super-) glue
- Small magnets (optional)
- Googly eyes (optional)

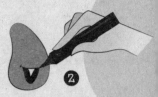

Instructions:

1. Give each side of your stone two coats of paint (allow to dry between coats).

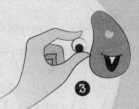

2. Draw or paint a monster mouth on your stones. You can use a paintbrush if you have a really steady hand, but a fine-tip marker is much easier.

3. Glue on googly eyes. Let glue dry overnight.

4. Leave your stone as it is to be used as a paperweight, or glue on magnets. The magnets should be strong, but not the super ones that are nearly impossible to move. Carefully glue on your magnet with superglue. Larger stones may require two magnets (make sure they are facing the right way to attract each other and not repel). Let the glue dry overnight.

5 Secrets to Being a Great Best Friend

1. KEEP YOUR WORD.

It sounds like a no-brainer, but the truth is, the closer you get to someone, the more likely you are to take them for granted. Do you often cancel prearranged plans with your BFF because you're too tired or not in the mood? Remind yourself it's a privilege to have a very best friend, and you should honor that by being as considerate and respectful as you would to a brand-new friend.

2. LISTEN.

When your friend is talking, try not to interrupt. If you have suggestions or comments, wait until she's done. Interrupting someone or cutting them off mid-sentence gives the message that her thoughts aren't important enough for you to listen to. It's natural to want to chime in when something pops into your head, but try to save it until she's finished.

3. DON'T LECTURE.

No one likes a know-it-all. Only offer your opinion if she asks for it. Instead of launching into a speech about what you would do in her situation, ask her questions like "That's a difficult situation to be in. What are you going to do about it?"

4. DON'T MAKE IT ALWAYS ABOUT YOU.

Even if your personality is naturally more outgoing and your friend is quieter, take the time to ask questions about her day and ask how she's feeling or what she wants to do.

5. BE HAPPY FOR HER.

If something great happens to your BFF, be happy! Instead of feeling jealous and sulking, *celebrate* with your friend. When it's your turn to celebrate, don't you want your BFF there at your side?

And most of all . . .

Be the friend you want to have!